Die Kitty Die

by Dan Parent and Fernando Ruiz

for Darwyn

DIE *Kitty* DIE! ™

STORY & ART
Fernando Ruiz & Dan Parent

INKS
Rich Koslowski and J. Bone

COLORS
Glenn Whitmore

LETTERS
Janice Chiang

ADDITIONAL ART
Gisele Lagace, J. Bone, & Bill Golliher

Fadi Hakim - Publisher
Keith WTS Morris - Production / Operations
Tony White - Supervising Editor / Media Co-ordinator
Kalman Andrasofszky - Creative Director

Die Kitty Die Deluxe Edition Vol. 1. © DAN PARENT & FERNANDO RUIZ 2016. Published by the Chapterhouse Comics Group™ 25 Skey Lane, Toronto, Ontario, Canada M6J 3V2. Contains material originally published in single magazine format as Die Kitty Die #1-4. Printed by Transcontinental, Beauceville, QC. Printed in Canada.

THE NEXT DAY...

YOU GOT A *DATE* WITH KITTY? *VA-VA-VA-VOOM!*

I KNOW. SHE'S A *KNOCKOUT!*

HAVE YOU *SEEN* THOSE *TORPEDOS?*

I'M GONNA *SEE* THEM IN ALL THEIR *NAKED GLORY* BY NIGHT'S END!

THAT NIGHT...

HE *LIKES* ME! HE'S BEEN *STARING* AT ME ALL NIGHT!

MAN! THOSE *MISSLES* ARE POINTING RIGHT AT *ME!*

LET'S *GO* FOR A DRIVE!

OKAY!

SO... IT'S *LOVELY* TONIGHT! WHAT A *BEAUTIFUL* MOON!

I *LOVE* THE WAY THE MOON *SHINES* ON...

...THOSE *GLORIOUS* KNOCKERS!!

WHAT? HOW DARE YOU!

I DON'T GET IT, *KITTY!* YOU'RE A *REAL LIFE WITCH* WITH *REAL* MAGIC POWERS! YOUR COMIC BOOK IS *BASED* ON YOU!

HOW COULD IT *NOT* BE SELLING?

I DON'T KNOW, MARA... BUT I'M *WORRIED...*

YOU DON'T MEAN THEY MIGHT ACTUALLY *CANCEL* YOUR BOOK, DO YOU?

I THINK IT COULD BE *WORSE* THAN *THAT...*

WORSE THAN *CANCELLATION?* WHAT COULD BE WORSE THAN *THAT?*

ALL THE *STUNTS* MY PUBLISHER MIGHT TRY TO *SAVE* MY BOOK.

WE'VE BEEN *DOWN* THIS ROAD *BEFORE...*

REMEMBER LAST YEAR WHEN THEY HAD ME GET *MARRIED?*

HEY! THAT WAS A *BIG DEAL!*

AT LONG LAST... *"KITTY THE TEEN WITCH GETS MARRIED!"* THAT ISSUE BECAME A COLLECTOR'S ITEM!

YOU *SHOULD* BE *CONCERNED*, KITTY! YOU NEVER KNOW WHAT THE HEADS OF *KITTY COMICS* ARE GOING TO DO WHEN THEY GET *DESPERATE*...

...BUT IF THEY HAVE YOU FIGHT *ZOMBIES* AGAIN, THINK OF *ME*! I CAN USE THE *WORK*!

OH, *DIPPY*...

I KNOW HOW TO TURN YOUR *BOOK* AROUND, KIT.

YOU *DO*, *RUDY*?!

YEP! A NEW *ADULT* KITTY BOOK COMPLETE WITH...

FULL NUDITY!

HEY!

BAMF

YOU *JERK*! HOW DID YOU DO THAT?

I READ KITTYS' *MAGIC BOOKS*! I'VE BEEN PRACTICING THAT *SPELL* FOR WEEKS!

YEAH, RUDYS' GOT A BUNCH OF *NAKED BARBIES* ALL OVER HIS ROOM NOW.

RUDY!

YOU SNEAKY LITTLE...

‹ULP!›

TOAD!

ZAP!

WHOA! LOOK AT ME!

HA! GEE, RUDY, YOU'RE PRETTY *CHIPPER* FOR A GUY WHO'S A *FROG* NOW.

HEY! IN ORDER TO *CHANGE* ME BACK, *KITTY* HAS TO *KISS* ME...

EWW! KEEP WAITING, YOU *GREEN GEEK!*

YOU BETTER HOPE *KITTY KISSES* YOU FAST, RUDY... 'CUZ ACCORDING TO HER...

...SHE DOESN'T HAVE MUCH *TIME LEFT!*

END CHAPTER 1

OUT OF ALL OF THEM, *KITTY* WAS THE *BIGGEST HIT!*

NOW WE CAN BARELY *GIVE* HER BOOKS AWAY!

DUUUUUUDE!!

...KITTY IS *DONE!* LIKE... SOOOO DONE! *TOTALLY!* NO *EF'S* ARE GIVEN FOR *KITTY!*

OKAY, *ACE,* YOU'RE MY EDITOR IN CHIEF. *WHAT* DO WE DO?

TWO WORDS, SKIP... *RE* AND *BOOT!*

RE BOOT KITTY?

TOTALLY!

LAST COMIC CON, I TALKED TO *GIOVANNI GOMEZ!*

HE WROTE A HIT MOVIE WHICH *MAYBE* THREE PEOPLE SAW LAST YEAR! HE'S TOTALLY STOKED TO WRITE *KITTY!*

HAS HE *EVER* WRITTEN A *COMIC BOOK?*

WHO *CARES?* JUST *ANNOUNCING* HIS *NAME* WILL GET US FIVE HUNDRED *LIKES* ON *SPACE BOOK!*

CHAPTER 3 HOME ALONE

RAVENCRAFT MANOR

POOF

?

Oh!

DIPPY! YOU *SCARED* ME!

HA! IT'S JUST *LIKE* ONE OF MY OLD CARTOONS!

♪ I JUST *WANNA* BE FRIENDS! ♪

YOU SEEMED REALLY DOWN AT THE *STORE.* I WANTED TO MAKE SURE YOU WERE *OKAY.*

AWW... THANKS, *DIPPY.*

I WAS JUST WONDERING WHAT TO *DO* NOW...

YOU MEAN FOR A *JOB?*

WELL, THERE'S *THAT.* I'VE BEEN *LIVING OFF* MY COMIC BOOK FOR YEARS AND IF IT *GOES...*

WELL, *THEN* I GUESS I'LL HAVE TO MAKE A *LIVING* SOMEWHERE *ELSE...*

...THERE AREN'T *MANY* PLACES YOU CAN GO, THOUGH...

...WHEN YOU'RE A *WITCH!*

Fashion designs by J.Bone

ASTRO COMIX

KITTY

399¢

DIE Kitty DIE!

NO. 2

Dan Parent.

DAN PARENT,

FERNANDO RUIZ

AND WHAT'S WORSE, HE'S *CRUSHED* THE TOWN OF *TINKERVILLE!*

THAT BUFFOON IS *SUPPOSED* TO BE GUARDING US...

INSTEAD HE GOT *HIGH* ON *DRAGONBERRIES* AND *PASSED OUT...*

RIGHT *ON* OUR TOWN..

WELL, I CAN TAKE *CARE* OF ERNIE...

AND I'LL *SWOOP* THROUGH TOWN AND *SEE* WHAT I CAN DO...

⨪UGH!⨪ YOU ARE ONE *BIG BOY!!!*

So... *THANKS* FOR BRINGING HIM *HOME,* KITTY!

I'LL *KEEP* MY EYE *ON* HIM!

AND *AWAY* FROM DRAGONBERRIES!

OWW!

And now back to the present...

BOO-TY CALL!

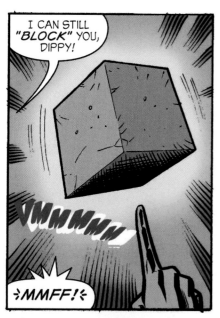

I CAN STILL "BLOCK" YOU, DIPPY!

MMMMM

÷MMFF!÷

YOU *DON'T* GET IT! YOU CAN'T *STOP* A GHOST!

OKAY... HEY! WHERE'D SHE GO?

Outside...

BAMF!

THIS IS *CRAZY!* DIPPY'S *REALLY* TRYING TO *KILL* ME!

BUT *WHY???*

HE IS *RIGHT!* HE'S A *GHOST!*

EVEN WITH *MAGIC* I DON'T KNOW IF I CAN *STOP* HIM...

...BUT I KNOW SOMEONE WHO *CAN!*

POOF

HI! IT'S *ME!*

I... I NEED YOUR *HELP...*

WHO YOU GONNA CALL?

ULP!

...THE *DEADLY TRIO?!*

YOU GONNA TAKE US *ALL* ON? YOU'RE PROBABLY NO STRANGER TO A LITTLE *THREE-ON-ONE* ACTION!

FATS, ARE YOU MAKING *DIPPY* DO THIS?

US? *NAH! DIS* WAS ALL *DA KID'S IDEA!*

HE'S ALWAYS BEEN A LITTLE *WUSS* TRYIN' TA BE *FRIENDS* WITH DA *LIVIN'*!

WHEN HE TOLD US 'BOUT DIS DEAL TA *KILL* YA...

...WELL WE COULDN'T BE *PROUDER!*

DEAL?! WHAT *DEAL?*

DON'T WORRY, *KITTY.* SOON YOU'LL BE *DEADER* THAN *WE* ARE...

...BUT MAYBE YOU CAN BE *REPRINTED* IN MY *NEW* BOOK!

I'M **WARNING** YOU, GUYS!

I **JUST** CALLED FOR **HELP!**

BIG **DEAL!** WHO'DJA CALL? DA **COPS?**

'S BEEN A WHILE **SINCE** I ATE **PORK!**

YOU GUYS **DON'T** GET IT! THIS ISN'T MY **CELL** PHONE...

...IT'S MY **HELL** PHONE!

HUH?

WHO D'YA CALL WIT **DAT?**

AWWW... NO....

...LI'L SATAN!!

THANKS FOR COMING ON SUCH **SHORT** NOTICE, **SATAN.**

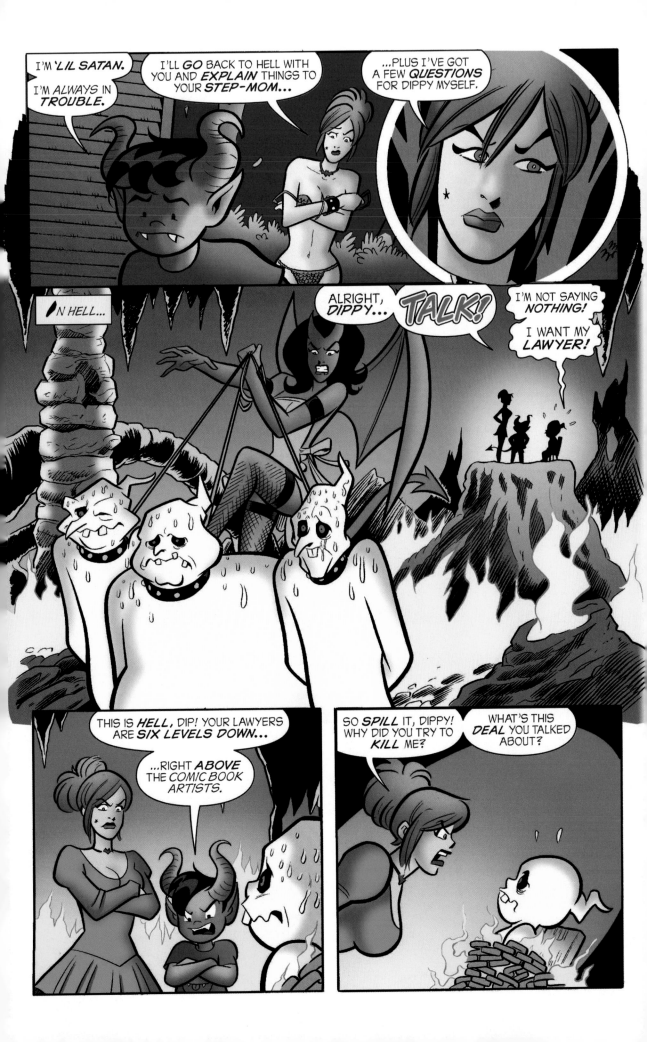

OUT WITH THE *OLD*...

IN WITH THE *NEW*.

So...

IT'S TRUE... IS IT *REALLY* TRUE?

I SAW IT ON *BLEEDING STOOL*!

IT *APPEARS* SO...

COMIX CORNER

WE'VE *LOST* OUR KITTY...

SHE WAS SUCH A SPECIAL *PERSON*... ER... *WITCH*!

YAY!

Cutesy n Wutesy

WE *NEVER* EVEN HAD A *CHANCE* TO GO OUT...

WE NEVER GOT TO *ACT* ON OUR *SEXUAL TENSION*...

SHE *MIGHT* HAVE BEEN A *SUPERSTAR*...

A *PUBLIC* FIGURE, A TALENTED *WITCH*...

BUT *KITTY*... SHE... SHE...

SHE WAS OUR *FRIEND*...

THE WORLD IS ABOUT TO *MEET* KITTY'S *REPLACEMENT!*

MEET KITTY'S *EVIL* COUSIN, OR AS I LIKE TO *CALL* HER...

KITTY'S KATWALK
MONSTER MAKEOVER

Fashion designs by J.Bone

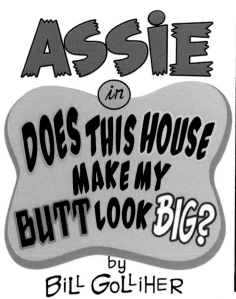

ASSIE in SNOW PROBLEM!

by BILL GOLLIHER

THE END

And now back to present day......

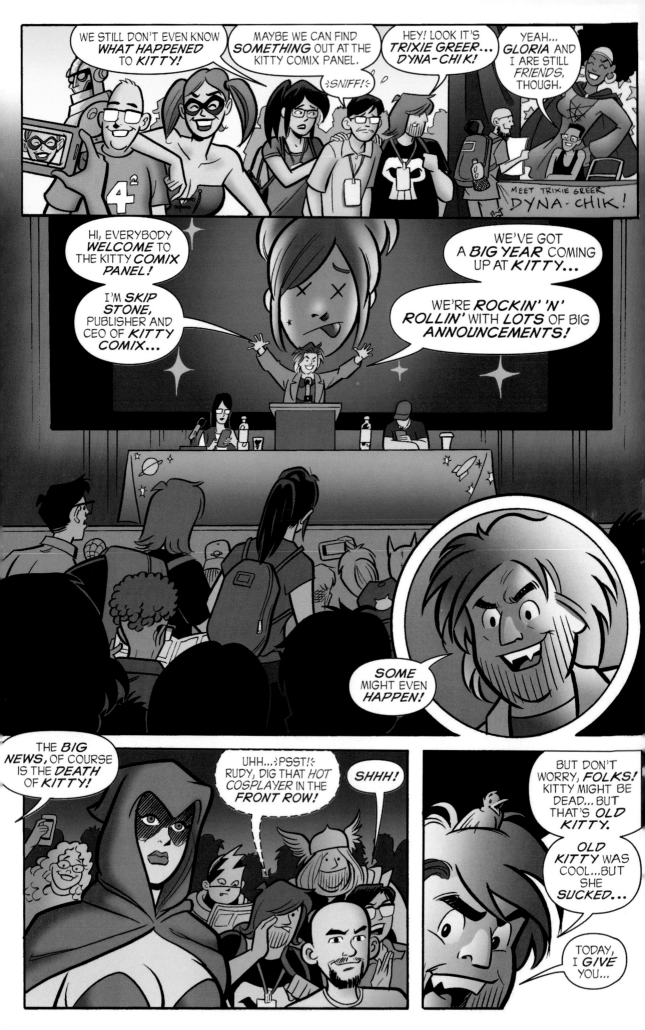

...AMERICAN GLORIA HAS ONLY *ONE SIDEKICK!*

700

COMIC

DYNA-CHIK!

HSSSSS

ALRIGHT, *KATTY*... THIS ONE'S A *WRAP!*

BAMF

NOT EVEN CLOSE, KITTY...

...NOT EVEN *CLOSE!*

GOOD TO SEE YOU AGAIN, *DYNA!* WHAT'S *WITH* THE *GUN?*

I GOT A SOLO SERIES COMING OUT. I'M A *VIGILANTE* IN A *ZOMBIE APOCALYPSE!*

HEY! *REMEMBER ME?*

RIDGE BLOCK

AMERICAN GLORIA'S BF
RIDGE BLOCK

KITTY! YOU'RE *ALIVE!*

HA! YOU SHOWED THOSE *SCUMBAG PUBLISHERS* OF *YOURS!*

NO, THEY'LL KEEP *TRYING* TO *KILL* ME...

...BUT NOW I HAVE TO *WONDER*...

...WHO WILL THEY SEND *NEXT?*

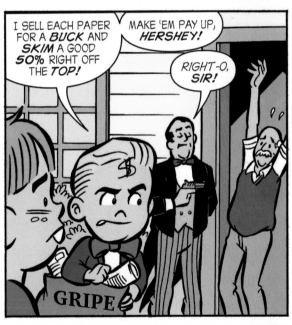

BECAUSE I'M FROM A *PRESTIGIOUS FAMILY*... WE HAVE TO LOOK OUR PART!

BUT I *MISS* MY APARTMENT NEAR THE *COMIC SHOP*.

AND I MISS MY *FRIENDS!*

I HAVE AN *IDEA!* LET'S HAVE SOME *FUN!* JUST YOU AND I.

LET'S RUN THE *LITTLE ELVES* OUT OF *TINKYTOWN!*

WHAT? WHY? THAT'S JUST SO *MEAN.*

HAR HAR

WE'RE *WITCHES!* THAT'S WHAT WE *DO.*

WELL, NOT ME! I'M A *GOOD* WITCH!!

GOOD! BAD! IT'S ALL *SUBJECTIVE!*

OH, DEREK! WHAT IS *IT* THAT I SEE IN *YOU?*

OH, *YEAH,* THAT'S IT...

CHAPTER 2: KITTY'S KATT HOUSE!

CAN'T WE JUST CALL THE *COPS?*

MIX CORNER

BOOKS • MAGAZINES • COLLECTIBLES

I MEAN *KITTY COMICS* HAS TRIED TO *KILL KITTY!*

THEY CAN'T JUST GET *AWAY* WITH *THAT!*

BUT HOW DOES ANYONE *PROVE* IT? THEY'VE JUST SENT A BUNCH OF *GHOSTS* AND A *CRAZY WITCH* TO TRY TO *KILL* HER.

AND THERE'S NO *PROOF* OF THIS *DEAL* TO GIVE ANYONE WHO KILLED ME THEIR *OWN COMIC BOOK.*

THE DEATH OF *Kitty*

KITTY DIES

CHAPTER 2 PART 6 OF 28

#28 OF 250 VARIANT COVERS

UH... *KITTY...?* IS THAT FOR YOU...?

UM... *YEAH...*

IT'S A *HEX MESSAGE!*

IT'S AN *INVITATION!*

IT'S FROM MY *EX-HUSBAND.*

HE WANTS TO *SEE* ME!

YOUR *EX-HUSBAND?!*

THAT *BUM?!*

WAITAMINUTE! WHICH *ONE?*

IT'S *DEREK!*

HE WANTS TO SEE ME AT OUR OLD *CASTLE.*

NO!

DON'T DO IT, *KITTY!*

THAT *DEREK GUY* WAS ALWAYS A *JERK!*

IT'S GOTTA BE A *TRAP!*

DO YOU THINK *KITTY COMICS* OFFERED *DEREK* HIS OWN *BOOK* TO *KILL* YOU?

MAYBE. I DON'T KNOW I COULD NEVER *TRUST* DEREK...

BUT I'M NOT *AFRAID* OF HIM!

BUT HE'S A *POWERFUL WARLOCK!*

I'VE ALWAYS BEEN *MORE POWERFUL.*

DEREK HAS ALWAYS *NEEDED* HIS MAGIC *WAND.*

IT'S THE SOURCE OF HIS *POWER!*

I CAN'T BELIEVE HE WOULD *HURT* ME, I'M GOING TO *SEE* HIM.

THEN WE'RE GOING *WITH* YOU!

AWWW... YOU GUYS ARE *THE BEST!*

LET'S GO!

BAMF!

AFRAID TO MEET ME *ALONE*, HUH?

WHADDAYA WANT, *DEREK*?

YOU COULD'VE BEEN MY *QUEEN*, KITTY...

...BUT YOU LEFT ME... AND FOR *WHAT*?

TO BE A *COMIC BOOK CHARACTER*?!

I LIKE MY *LIFE*, DEREK.

WELL, *THIS* IS AWKWARD!

FINE! IF NOT *ME* THEN... MAYBE ONE OF THESE GUYS...

OH NO!

YOU REMEMBER THE *GUYS*...

...WOLFGANG McINTYRE...

WOOF!

...FRANKLIN McSTEIN...

...ROCKSTAR MILES PUCK...

...AND ERNIE DOLLOP, C.P.A...

TAX PREPARATIONS ARE MY *SPECIALTY*.

UMM... *WHO* ARE THESE GUYS, *KITTY*?

MY *HUSBANDS*...

ALL OF THEM?

AND *I* CAN'T GET A *SHOT* AT HER?!

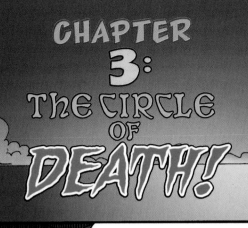

CHAPTER 3: THE CIRCLE OF DEATH!

WE'VE GOT YOU, KITTY...

...WE'VE GOT YOU!

I NEEDED FIVE ANGRY MEN TO CAST THIS PENTAGRAM SPELL AND TRAP YOU.

FORTUNATELY, YOU'VE BEEN SCREWING OVER LOTS OF MEN FOR YEARS!

GETTING THE FIVE OF US TOGETHER WASN'T HARD.

WHAT CAN WE DO?

WELL, I THINK I PEED ON MYSELF!

I'M CHECKING MY MAGIC SPELLS APP!

AND I'M GONNA EAT THESE *KIDS* AS AN APPETIZER...

...BEFORE I EAT *KITTY!*

RUDY! DON'T YOU HAVE *ANY SPELLS* YOU CAN USE?

AHH... I...I *THINK* I CAN MAKE HIM *NAKED!* *

*DKD #1

‡GRRRR‡... FRANK... SQUEEZE...

THA'S IT, MATE! LET'S SHOW 'ER 'T AIN'T *CRICKET* T' TRIFLE WITH A *MAN'S AFFECTIONS!*

WAIT, GENTLEMEN, LET'S...

WE'VE WAITED LONG ENOUGH *WARLOCK!*

IT'S TIME WE *CASHED OUT* AND GOT A *RETURN* ON OUR *INVESTMENT!*

CRUSH HER, *MONSTER!*

CRUSH HER!

SO BE IT, *ACCOUNTANT...*

SO BE IT...

‡GRRR‡...

UGN!

‡HUFF PUFF‡ ...! I... I'VE GOT TO RUN AWAY BEFORE *KITTY* CATCHES ME!

SHE'LL FREEZE MY *ACCOUNTS!*

SHE'LL HAVE ME *AUDITED!*

HUH?!

HOLD IT, POINDEXTER... C'MERE...

YOU!!

I'VE HAD MY *EYE* ON *YOU!*

ULP!

I DON'T GET IT! HOW DID *KITTY* GET HER *MAGIC* BACK?

DON'T YOU *SEE?* IT MUST'VE BEEN *DEREK!*

HE *SABOTAGED* THE *SPELL!*

HUH? BUT *WHY* WOULD HE DO *THAT?*

LOOK!

...I THINK *THAT'S* THE ANSWER.

Fashion designs by J.Bone

KITTY'S PAL
RUDY
IN
"LOVE POTION NO. ....MINE!"

HEY, KITTY!! YOU *HOME?*

I'LL BE RIGHT *OUT*, RUDY!

NO *RUSH*, MY *CRUSH!*

HMM... ONE OF KITTY'S MAGIC SPELL BOOKS... I'LL JUST *TAKE* A *PEEK!*

OOH! A SPELL TO MAKE ME *IRRESISTIBLE* TO WOMEN!

I GOTTA TRY THIS!

"OHWA TA GOO SIAM!"

HIYA, SEXY!

AAAAAHH!!

AAAAACCKKK!!

RUDY..? GEE! WHERE DID HE GO?

C'MON, SKINNY! PUT SOME *TONGUE* INTO IT!

SOB!!!

THE END

Kitty in **D&D** and **DOUBLE D!**

COMIX CORNER

Comics ★ Games ★ Books ★ Collect

OPEN

THE *GORR-OCTOPUS* IS *ATTACKING!*

WHAT DO YOU DO, *GRONK THE DWARF?*

⸘ULP!⸘ I... I USE MY *PLUS TEN ENCHANTED SWORD!*

WAIT, *JIM!* I'M A *MAGIC USER! THIRD* LEVEL! I'M GOING TO USE A *SPELL...*

AMPIRETTA

CAPTAIN AWESOME

YOU *CAN'T! MAGIC* IS *INEFFECTIVE* AGAINST *GORR-OCTOPI!*

WHAT?! YOU MADE THAT UP, *RUDY!*

NOPE! CHECK THE *MONSTER MANUAL!* ROLL THE *BONES, GRONK!*

OKAY, HERE GOES...

shake shake

D'OH!

CRITICAL FAILURE!

GRONK *FALLS!* NOW THE GORR-OCTOPUS *STRIKES!*

EEP!

shake shake

CRITICAL SUCCESS!

HE *HITS!*

NOOO!

DOUBLE DAMAGE! TAKE *TWO HUNDRED* POINTS OF DAMAGE!

WHAA...?! I'M *DEAD!*

≑SOB≑ I'VE BEEN PLAYING *GRONK* SINCE I WAS EIGHT!

HE'S GOT A *GIRLFRIEND* WITH A *COMLINESS* OF *20!*

HE'S GOT *KIDS!*

HE BETTER HAVE A *GRAVE* 'CUS HE BE *DEAD* NOW, *LOSER!*

RUDY!

YOU'RE THE *DUNGEON MASTER!* YOU'RE *SUPPOSED* TO BE *NEUTRAL!*

NEUTRAL SHMUTRAL! RUDY'S A *NAZI DM!*

OKAY, MAGIC USER! YOU'RE HIT BY A *SPELL!* YOU MUST *KISS* THE *DM!*

WHAT?! I DON'T EVEN GET A *SAVING THROW...*

NOPE...

...THE SPELL *COMPELLS* YOU!

WHOA!

KITTY?!?

DUDE... ARE... ARE YOU GUYS G... GONNA ...LIKE... MAKE *SEX* RIGHT HERE?

BUMP!

FLIP

HEY! WAIT A MINUTE!

I SHOULD'VE *KNOWN!* THIS IS ONE OF *KITTY'S SPELL BOOKS!* RUDY STOLE ANOTHER ONE OF HER BOOKS!

HE'S PROBABLY BEEN USING IT TO *CONTROL* THE *DICE...*

AND NOW TO *CONTROL KITTY!*

Kitty Gallery **PART 1**

Kitty Gallery PART 2

Kitty Gallery PART 3

Be
my
friend

Kitty Gallery PART 4

Kitty's CAULDRON!

THE PLACE TO SHARE YOUR THOUGHTS ABOUT ALL THINGS KITTY!

WE WANT YOUR THOUGHTS AND COMMENTS ON *"DIE KITTY DIE!"* WE ALSO WOULD LOVE TO SEE YOUR SKETCHES AND FASHION IDEAS TOO!

YOU CAN SEND ANY COMMENTS, IDEAS, SKETCHES, JUNK MAIL, NUDE PHOTOS (kidding!) TO:

dan@astrocomix.com
fernando@astrocomix.com

THANK YOU!!

We couldnt have done this without the help of our kickstarter backers! Special thanks to:

Carl Anders Aabø, Robert Adam II, Clint Adams, Jonci Aguillard, Roberto Aguirre-Sacasa, Ahad Al Saud, Adam Alamo, John Albinsson, Martin Alderette, Alfredo, Brigid Allanson, Sean Allen, Greg Allen, Carolyn Altieri, Hisham Alvi, Alyssa, Jay Amabile, Samantha Amyot, John Tore Andersen, Brian Andersen, andertoons,Steve Andreski, Andrew, McKenna E. Andrews, Ivan Marcondes Antonio, Nathan Archer, Albert Aribaud, Gary Arkell, David Aronoff, Charles Atencio, William Austin, Jimmy Autrey, Ed Aycock, James Azrael.

Matthew B., Sachin Bahal, Jim Bailey, JB Balen, Daryl Ball, Drew Bancroft, Steve Barghusen, Lance Barnett, Mike Barreiro, Jeff Batista, Dallan Baumgarten, Jeff Beck, Ákos Bedekovics, Jens Bejer Pedersen, Randy Belanger, Todd Belton, Eyal Benezra, Paul Benincasa, Keith Benson, Jef Berard, Frank Bergdoll, Yvette Beshier, Steven Best, George Bevis, Drew Bittner, Steven Bloom, Raymond Blum, David Blumer, Martin Boruta, Athos Bousvaros, Brainiac187,Steven Brandon, Jack Briglio, Scott Brinkman, Jason Broadley, Fred Bronaugh, Jason Brooks, Ted Brown, Christopher Buch, Chris Buchner, Christian Buckingham, Dennis Budd, Tom Burbine, James Burdo, Jonathan Burgers, Thomas Burton, Kurt Busiek.

Annie C., Michael C., Gene Cahill, Mario Candelaria, John Cannan, Leroy (Larry) Capasso, Gabriel Carino, Johanna Draper Carlson, Scott Carnes, Jerry Carr, Brett Carreras, Erik W. Carter, Dave Carter, Alina Casales, Kelly Cassidy, Catherine, cathulhu, Ken Catino, Rhys Cavanagh, CDK!, Chad, Keith Champagne, Larry Cheng, Cheshi, Steve Chino, Tyler & Wendy Chin-Tanner, Zan Christensen, Christian, Nathan Chung, Robert Chute, Michele Cioffi, Cody Clark, Breanna Clark, Adam Coffin, Coleman, Ben Coleman, Robert Collins, Christopher Collins, Tina Como, Alaric Connell, Matt Conner, CrazyGood Conner, David Conner, Alex Cook, Charles Cook, J Cope, Aaron Corff, Hannah Corpuz, Brett Cosby, Sean Costigan, Kelsy Cowan, Daniel Crosier, Adan Cueva, Wally Czyzniak.

dadams1,Corey Dalton, Shad Daly, Dawn Daniell, Abate David, William Patrick Davis, Greg Dawson, DCQ, Luc de Chancenotte, J. Robert Deans, Paul DeBaldo, Tom DeFalco, Paula Del Cid, Jim Demonakos, John Dermer, Paul Dini, John Dodds, Carlton Donaghe, Daniel Donnelly, Mark Doolan, Leshia Doucet, Doug, Joseph Dougherty, David Drabik, Frank Drabik, Evan Dressel, Liam Duffy, Gary Dunaier, Dennis Dunkman, Brad Dunlap, Michael Durband.,

Roland Edwards Jr., Kristin El, Elizabeth, Michael Ellis, Elyn, Emily, P. Kristen Enos, Patricia Erdely, Eric, Solvi Ericson, Erik, Linn Eriksson, Errberry, Marcus Eskow, cyborg etrigan, David Evanetz, Sandy Evans, Ron Evans.

Skip & Wendy Farrell, Heather Farrington, fddm, Stephen Feely, Ajai Fel, Johannes Felbauer, Daisy Fentiman, James Ferguson, Clay Fernald, Angie Fernot, Martin Ferretti, Donald Ferris, Alec J. Fields, Erin Firth, Ellen Fleischer, Nigel Fletcher, Philip C. Ford, Franco, Freddy, Derek Freeman, John Fritz, Jan Fuellemann, Timothy Fuller, Gregory Furr.

Aaron G., Sam Gafford, Charles Gaines-Hager, John Gallagher & Kids Love Comics, William Galvan, KE1 Games, Oscar Andrés Zaragoza García, Joe Garofolo, Peter A. Gehrmann, Aaron Gell, Erin Germain, Dave Gibbons, Dennis Gillund, Marc Goldberg, Jessica Lynn Goodwin, Michael Gordon, Niall Gordon, Matthew Gore, Carl Gould, Neil Graham, Michael Gravely, Grax Domain, David Gray, Peter Gray, Bruce Gray, Garrett Green, David Greenberg, The Grey, Grubnash, Jeffrey Grzybowski, Joe Gualtieri, Eric Guerber, Zane Gulley, George Gustines.

Robert Hack, Craig Hackl, Helfried Haider, Eric Hall, Will Hall, William Halpin, Rob Hamilton, Martin Hand, Russell J. Handelman, Ben Handin, Ayanni Hanna, Cameron Hansen, Steven Harbron, Michael Harmon, Sheryl Harris, Wally Hastings, Rick Hatch, Hayden, Kaleb Hazen, Darryl Heine, Thomas Helget, Harald Hellerud, Keith Hendricks, S. Steven Hendricks, Edmond Peter Hennessy, Jennifer Henning, Craig Henshaw, Paul M. Herkes, Ricardo Hernandez, Brian Hickok, Joshua Hilderbrad, Charlotte Hillery, Angela Hix, Richard Hodgson, Heather Holden, Agust Holmgeirsson, Jarrod Hoogendam, Daniel Hould, Ryan Howe, Hoyt, Thomas Hsieh, Hugo, imPhotoGraphics Design, Matthew Isaac.

Guardian J, J3H, Joseph Jackson, Amy Lynn Jackson, Matt Jacobs, Jannis, Paul Jarman, Jason, Jason, jbowtie, Clint Jenkins, Will Jenkins, Paul Jeromack, Jim, Joel, Reino Johansson, Ostrander John, Alex Johnson, Fred Johnson, Jeff Johnson, Rankin Johnson, Brendan Jones, jordo37, Adam Juda, Minkyu Jung, Sage Jurado, JustChris, k8207dz, Josh K., William K., Jeremy Kahn, D.W. Kann, Andrew Kaplan, Kassandralove, Katerater, Nick Katradis, Michael Kauffman, Fred Kaufmann, Kcbasher, Robert Keele Jr., Keeper3, Nathan Kellen, Kelsey, Kendal, Seán Kenneally, Wim Keppens, Joe Kersavage, Barbara Randall Kesel, Boon Khai, Bryan Khoo, Trevor Kimball, Matt Kimery, Patrick King, Stephon Kirkpatrick, Kevin Dale Kirmse, Kisai, Nicolaj 'Chico' Klitbo, Kyle Kondas, Jim Kosmicki, Winston Kou, Kracalactaka, Øystein Andres Krogsæter, Robert Krygier, Eric P. Kurniawan, Kyle.

Peter Lange, Cory Laub, Matthew Lazorwitz, Thomas Brendan Maughan Leahy, John Leasure, Amber Leedham, Leete, Nicolas Legare, Laurent Lehmann, Adam Leibig, Tasha Turner Lennhoff, Patrick LeRoy, Adam Lewinson, Brandon Lieu, Alex Lilley, Wei-Jiun Lim, Stefan Linden, Karl-Erik Lindkvist, David Lizewski, Ralph Llano, Jessie Loflin, Jay Lofstead, Daniel Lovasz, Jeffrey Low Dog, JP Lucas, David Lumsdon, Chris Lundin, Freddy Lupus, Eirik Lutro.

Steve M., John MacLeod, Jay Magnum, Joanna Maharaj, Mal, Tom Mandrake, Chris Manvell, Jaclyn Marques, Scott Martin, Christian Martinez, Matt, Garth Matthams, Tóth Mátyás, Josh Mawdsley, Max, Nick May, Marci McCann, Robert McCann, Nicholas McCaskie, Derek McCaw, Jim McClain, Mark McConnell, Riqui McCoy, Mark McCracken, Danielle McCrady, Andrew McDougall, Ken McGuire, Greg McKee, Andrew McLean, Tim Meakins, Melanie, Tom Michael, Lauren Michele, Steve Miller, Matthew Mitchell, Robert Mitchell, Jodi Moisan, Monkeywrench, Mark Montgomery, Monty, Evan D. Moore, Patrick Moreau, Seth Morris, James Morrison, Walter Moy, Thomas Mueller, TJ Mueller, Joe Murray, Blake Muxo.

Ken N., Helge Nareid, Aris Tara Nath, Roger Needham, William Nelson, Armond Netherly, Peggy Ng, Nichole, Brooks Nichols, Hope Nicholson, Jesse Noble, Paul Nordland.

Michael Obert, Rob O'Brien, Eric O'Connor, Bill ODonnell, CJ Oechsle, Rik Offenberger, Evonne Okafor, Rod Ollerenshaw.

Jeff Pacitto, Paradox Girl, Real & Helen Parent, Johnny Parker, Raymond Parungao, Michelle Titus Parylak, Rene Passarieu, Jasper Patch, patientlywaiting, Trey M. Patterson, Robert Paul, Rick Paula, Sean Peacock, Louie Pearlman, Damien Pearson, David & Tricia Pedro, David Peeler, Michael Pellerito, Tyrone Pemberton, Jason Penney, Andrew Pepoy, Ernest Pereira, Matthew Perry, John Peters, Scott Petersen, Blake Petit, Gary Phillips, Craig Phillips, John Picone, Bryan Pittard, Pixie Trix Comics, James Ponce, Ge Pop, Chad Porter, Ray Powell, Doug Prinzivalli, Andrew Purkiss, James Purves, Pyros, Chris Quinn, Quint.

Chris Raab, Gary Raiche, Danielle Ramirez, Gregory Ramos, , Raskolnikov, Janessa Ravenwood, Rawnzilla, Reality Happens, Fábio Redivo, Chris Rednour, William W. Refsland, Aleesa Regan, Dean Reilly, RevBob, Revek, Ana Reyes, Aaron Reynolds, Jeremiah Rice, Richard, Richard, Rlaein, Drew Tynan Robbins, Rafer Roberts, Robin, Dennis F. Rogers, Crystal Rollins, Thomas Root, Mike Rooth, Adrian Ropp, Geoff Rosengren, Jamie Rotante, Steve Rotterdam, Steven Rowe, Dennis Roy, Rene Roy, Fernando Ruiz, Adriane Ruzak, Ryan.

Jeremiah Sabadoz, saipaman, Kucho Sanchez, Saodhar, Randy Sauve, Elliott Sawyer, Erin Sayers, Schaefges,Bruce Schalcher, Scott Schaper, Jeff Schroeder, Greg Schwartz, Jerome Scott, Jim Scott, Kris Scott, Sean, Alex Segura, Timothy Seltman, Ari Shapiro, Larry Shell, Shelli, Allison Sheridan, Robert Shimizu, siggjen, Simon, Ayşegül Sınav, Jerry Siskind, Cameron Smith, Andy Smith, Vanessa Solis, Mikhail Solovyev, Cole Sorensen, Paulo Souza Jr., Alan Sparrow, Kirk Spencer, Josh Stafford, Stan!, Chris Stewart, Tom Stillwell, Brandon Strang, Strange Adventures, Brett 'DJ Archangel' Strassner, Devin Straus, Rand Sugano, sweetmusic_27, swi7ch.

Sean Teague, Teeje, The Artifice Club, TheBigK, Mikkel Thomas, Cecelia Barrett Thomas, Nathan Thompson, John Tinkess, Jason R. Tippitt, Michael Riber Tolstrup, Max Torres, Daniel Townsend, Jay Towslee, Jimmy Tran, Max Traver, Dawn Trojan, Jon Trouten, Tuebor, Blaine & Marina Tufts, Marina Tufts, Sam Tweedle, Tymothy,.

Scott Umberger, Scott Underwood, Al Urrutia, Robert Usarek, Michael E. Uslan. Roch Vaillancourt, Josh Van Arsdale, Elizabeth Velazquez, Dan Veltre, Aaron Vietri, Andrew Vine, Philip Vint, Zack Viola, Kyle Voltti.

Eric Wadsworth, Henry Wagner, Peter Walbrun, Stacy Walker, Bradley Walker, Bill Walko, Stephen Walkup, Gary Waltz, Andrew Ward, Vaughan Ware, Duane Warnecke, Judah Warshaw, Randolph Washington Jr., Stacey Watson, Shannon Weathers, Markus Weber, Robert Weldon, Wellender, Thomas Werner, Matthew Wernsman, Bruce White, Jesse White,

Die Kitty Die

An Introduction and a Thank You

As I write this, less than a year has passed since that fateful plane trip to Dallas where Dan Parent and I first thought of the idea for what would become Die Kitty Die. In that remarkably short span of time, we hammered out the Die Kitty Die premise, we launched and waged an incredibly successful Kickstarter campaign, we wrote and drew all four issues, and we signed with Chapterhouse Comics to publish and distribute it all. It's been a busy year!

It's also been an overwhelmingly gratifying undertaking. For a long time, Dan and I had wanted to collaborate on a project together. We wanted something that we could creatively control and own completely. It's been an incredibly fun (if intense) process, and everyday we're surprised we're actually doing it. Of course, this entire process would not have been possible at all without all the help and support that we have received from many many people. A lot of fans, friends, and family have rallied to our side to make Die Kitty Die happen, and we would like to take a moment to thank a few special people who have really gone above and beyond for us.

First, we really need to thank our friend Adam Alamo and that great bunch on the Fans Of Archie Facebook page. Adam was a huge donor to our Kickstarter campaign but he was also one of our single biggest supporters, and worked tirelessly to spread word of Die Kitty Die. He shared our posts and updates relentlessly, and even started a Fans of Astrocomix Facebook page (which everyone should join if you haven't already!) Through Adam, we met other loyal supporters, like Sean Allen and Jim Bailey, who have also helped us tremendously.

We need to give a special thanks to our behind-the-scenes tech guy and webmaster, Justin Salvato. Very soon after Dan and I committed to this crazy idea, Justin hit the ground running and started the Die Kitty Die and Astrocomix websites. He has generously and tirelessly been our engineer and our advisor on all technical matters. He filmed and edited our Kickstarter video. The poor guy, we sure didn't give him much to work with, and he still made us at least sound sane.

Without a doubt, one of the key advantages on our side has been our relationship with the incredible, Gisele Lagace. A fellow Archie veteran, and the creator of the phenomenally successful Pixie Trix Comix brand of webcomix, Gisele has been our friend and our guide throughout this entire process. She has taken us both by the hand and generously shared her vast, considerable expertise in all matters concerning publishing and Kickstarter. There is no doubt that we could have achieved the success that we did without Gisele on our side. I seriously question if we would have succeeded at all. She reviewed everything we did, and often rewrote entire chunks of our campaign. Her friendship is truly a much appreciated blessing.

We'd like to thank Fadi Hakim and Tony White at Chapterhouse Comics for believing in the property, and offering to help us push it to greater heights.

I need to thank my spouse Carolyn for all her patience.. With our crazy convention schedules, and insane work hours, she has demonstrated exceptional patience. This Kickstarter Campaign alone was almost a full time job, and with all those rewards still ahead of us, the job isn't over. It's a great comfort to have our families firmly with us, and helping us through this incredible undertaking.

Lastly, as a personal note, I have to extend a profound thank you to the best friend and partner anyone could ask for, my pal, Dan Parent. We've spent many many weekends traveling together to different conventions across North America. We've had many five hour lunches, and dinners, hammering out Kitty's adventures. This crazy idea would never have gone anywhere if we didn't have such compatible sensibilities, and got along so well. I know without a doubt I could not have done half of what you do. You're my rock!

There are a lot of people I can continue to talk about and thank. I apologize if we haven't made a special mention here, but if we called out everyone, our page count would skyrocket through the roof, and we would need a whole new Kickstarter campaign to pay for it! Rest assured, you have our deepest thanks, and if we see you at one of our many convention appearances, we'll definitely let you know what you mean to us.

Thank you.

Die Kitty Die

Thoughts and Appreciations

Well, what a year it's been. When Fernando and I decided to launch our own project, I don't think we had any idea how much work it would be. Or how gratifying it would be!

Launching your own project can be a scary thing. You never know how it's going to be accepted. And even if you do get it funded, can you pull it off? Well, in this case, I'm so happy to say we did it. With the help of our Kickstarter backers first and foremost! The fact that we have so many supporters is simply amazing! But of course, there are those who deserve special thanks!

Gisele Lagace was our guardian angel, supporter and go to person for EVERYTHING! She runs a hugely successful company of her own (pixietrixcomix), and has run a couple successful kickstarters. So we learned a lot from her. We stumbled a couple of times, but she set us straight! And she also contributed beautiful work to the project. And on top of it all, she's a great friend!

And of course there's the one and only Adam Alamo. A huge supporter of ours, he promotes our work across all social media platforms. He has spread the word of DIE KITTY DIE like the gospel! And his cohorts Jim Bailey and Sean Allen were always there with their support. And Fred Bronaugh, we can't forget you!

A big help to us on the project is my good friend Justin Salvato. He has managed our websites and social media pages. He also helped with our kickstarter and is always there to help . I've been friends with Justin since the days he was my boxing coach (poor guy had his work cut out for him then too!)

I'd also like to thank the folks at Chapterhouse Comics for taking us on as our publishers. Tony White and Fadi Hakim had so much faith in our project and have given us a good home to produce more Kitty adventures . We're so excited to work with them!

I owe the most thanks to my family. Kathy, Alex and Adam have been the most supportive family a guy could have. They've put up with all the weekends on the road, plus all the ridiculous late hours working on Kitty and the kickstarter. Kathy has been there all the way with me, she has been my rock since we were kids growing up in Vermont. This poor girl didn't know what she was in for! She has been my partner, therapist, cheerleader….I could go on. And the kids , you're always there to support your Dad. I'm blessed to have such a great family, and I love you all so much.

Oh yeah! There's one more person I have to thank! It's this Fernando Ruiz fella! What can I say about the F-Man? He is without a doubt the best friend I have ever had. We have always had a strong connection, always been able to talk for hours on end about all our interests and hobbies. We share a sensibility that is very strong. We've traveled the country together, shared many hotel rooms (keep your mind out of the gutter!) I can always count on Fernando on a personal and professional level. Fernando, did I ever tell you that you are the wind beneath my wings? Ha ha. I'm joking, but I'm not! Fernando is THE BEST!!

The other person I'm so thankful for on this project was the contribution from my favorite artist and biggest inspiration in the comic book world, the incredible Darwyn Cooke. The fact that he agreed to do our cover to the hardcover meant the world to us. A true gentleman and friend, I have been so honored to know this genius. And genius is not a word I throw around much, but he truly is one. It was crushing that during the production of this book Darwyn passed away at the young age of 53. But even though he was ill, he made sure he followed through on delivering us the cover art in time (with the help of the awesome Michael Cho). Darwyn's contribution means the world to me. I will cherish him forever. Thank you Darwyn.

So, here we go! It's DIE KITTY DIE time!

Dan Parent

Hugs & Kisses ...
xoxo, Kitty